LITERACY
FOR AGES
5-6

Ten Minute Tests

CONTENTS

Louis Fidge

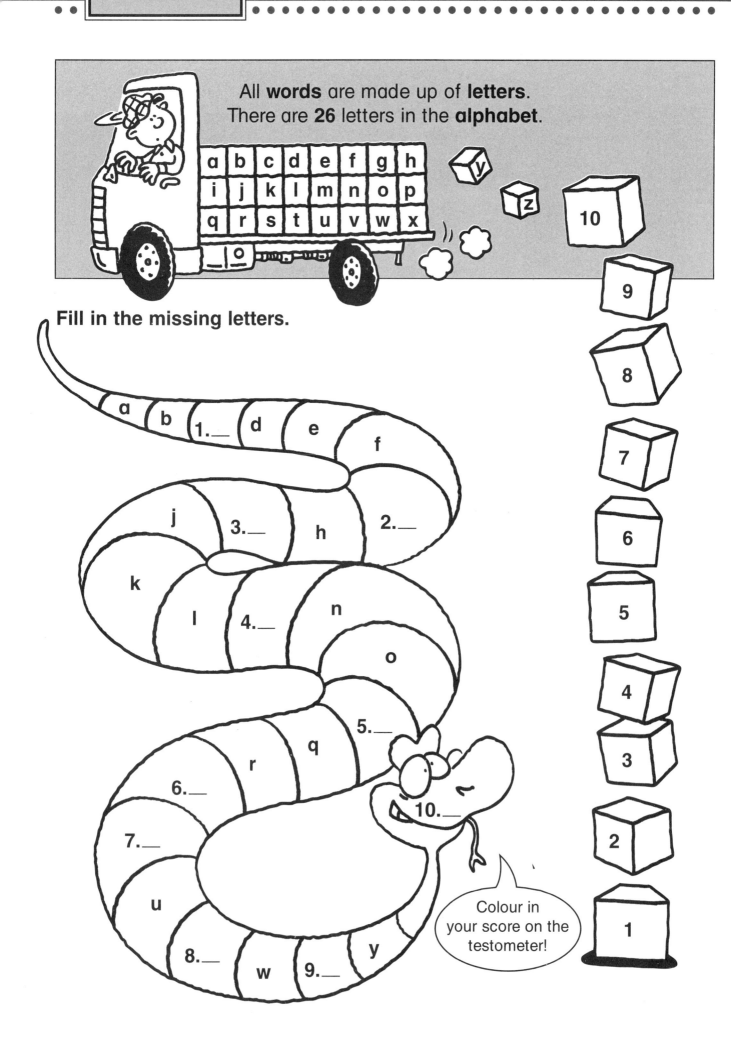

All **words** are made up of **letters**.
There are **26** letters in the **alphabet**.

a b c d e f g h
i j k l m n o p
q r s t u v w x

Fill in the missing letters.

a
b
1.___
d
e
f
2.___
h
3.___
j
k
l
4.___
n
o
5.___
q
r
6.___
7.___
u
8.___
w
9.___
y
10.___

Colour in your score on the testometer!

The sound of the **first letter** of each of these words is the **same**.

sun   saw   sink

Chose one of these letters to start each word.

m   p   h

1. ____eg

2. ____an

3. ____op

4. ____in

5. ____at

6. ____ut

7. ____en

8. ____op

9. ____ug

10. ____en

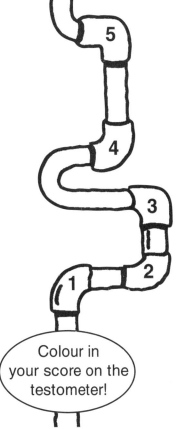

Colour in your score on the testometer!

We use **letters** to make **words**.

Colour in your score on the testometer!

b + a + t = bat

Do these sums. Write the words you make.

1. s + a + d = _____

2. d + i + g = _____

3. b + a + g = _____

4. t + o + p = _____

5. l + e + g = _____

6. f + o + x = _____

7. n + e + t = _____

8. t + u + b = _____

9. d + o + g = _____

10. j + u + g = _____

Many pictures have **labels** to help you.

ear
eye
nose
whiskers
tail
leg

Write the correct name under each animal.

| monkey | goat | horse | tiger | kangaroo |
| donkey | bear | zebra | camel | panda |

1. _____   2. _____   3. _____

4. _____   5. _____   6. _____

7. _____   8. _____

9. _____

Colour in your score on the testometer!

10. _____

A **sentence** must make **sense**.

I to hop like. ☒   I like to hop. ☑

Write the words in order to make some sentences.

1.   sun yellow. The is   _____

2.   green. is grass The   _____

3.   read. like to I   _____

4.   lay eggs. Hens   _____

5.   lion A roar. can   _____

6.   raining. is It   _____

7.   in You water. swim   _____

8.   ball. You a kick   _____

9.   door The shut. is   _____

10. stripes. A has tiger   _____

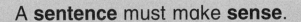

Test 6   Missing words

A **sentence** must make **sense**.

A roars. [X]

A lion roars. ✓

Choose the best word to finish each sentence.

| elephant | sun | money | cup | kangaroo |
| banana | star | spade | bike | umbrella |

1. You ride a _____ .

2. The _____ shines.

3. A _____ twinkles.

4. You spend _____ .

5. You eat a _____ .

6. A _____ hops.

7. You need an _____ in the rain.

8. You drink from a _____ .

9. An _____ has a trunk.

10. You dig with a _____ .

Colour in your score on the testometer!

10
9
8
7
6
5
4
3
2
1

The sound of the **last letter** of each of these words is the **same**.

pen   pin   pan

Colour in your score on the testometer!

Choose one of these letters to finish each word.

t   g   p

1. ba____

2. ma____

3. zi____

4. cu____

5. ha____

6. wi____

7. ne____

8. do____

9. ru____

10. po____

We sometimes **group** words together. These are all **birds**.

hen   parrot   sparrow

Colour in your score on the testometer!

bike   rocket   helicopter   bus   aeroplane

boat   yacht   car   ship   lorry

Sort these things into groups.

Things that go on land.

1. _____   2. _____

3. _____   4. _____

Things that fly in the sky.   Things that go in the water.

5. _____   8. _____

6. _____   9. _____

7. _____   10. _____

We can **build** words from **letters** and **groups of letters**.

b + ag
bag

r + ag
rag

w + ag
wag

Colour in your score on the testometer!

Do these sums. Write the words you make.

1. f + an = _____

2. s + ix = _____

3. v + an = _____

4. n + od = _____

5. l + eg = _____

6. r + od = _____

7. p + eg = _____

8. c + ut = _____

9. m + ix = _____

10. n + ut = _____

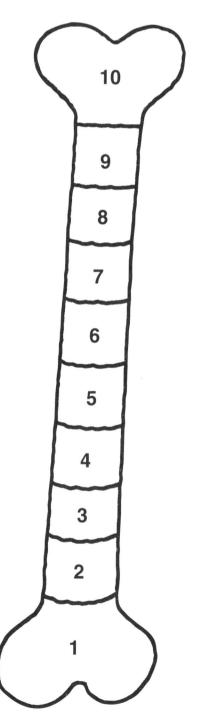

10
9
8
7
6
5
4
3
2
1

The sound of the **middle letter** of each of these words is the **same**.

pan   bat   bag

Colour in your score on the testometer!

Choose the correct middle letter to make each word.

a	o
1. j__m

u	a
2. t__p

u	o
3. l__g

o	u
4. b__n

u	e
5. t__b

o	i
6. s__b

i	e
10

7. t__n

e	i
8. t__n

a	i
9. b__b

e	a
10. j__t

10
9
8
7
6
5
4
3
2
1

A **sentence** often begins with a **capital letter** and ends with a **full stop**.

The girl fell off her bike.

Colour in your score on the testometer!

Write these sentences correctly.

1. the rain falls _____

2. a tree grows tall _____

3. the sky is blue _____

4. my cup is full _____

5. a cow moos _____

6. we like books _____

7. you bang a drum _____

8. it is sunny _____

9. a ball is round _____

10. i like to sing _____

Some words end with **double letters**.

Colour in your score on the testometer!

Pass the ball.

	doll	off	bell	
hill	toss	puff	fall	
	hiss	cuff	fuss	

Write the words that end with ff.

1. _____   2. _____

3. _____

Write the words that end with ll.

4. _____   5. _____

6. _____   7. _____

Write the words that end with ss.

8. _____   9. _____

10. _____

Many words end in **ck**.

Colour in your score on the testometer!

A du**ck** says qua**ck**.

Do these sums. Write the words you make.

1. b + a + ck = _____

2. p + a + ck = _____

3. n + e + ck = _____

4. p + e + ck = _____

5. k + i + ck = _____

6. s + i + ck = _____

7. l + o + ck = _____

8. d + o + ck = _____

9. l + u + ck = _____

10. s + u + ck = _____

Many words end in **ng** and **nk**.

I can si**ng**.

Colour in your score on the testometer!

I can thi**nk**.

Find and write the ng **or** nk **words that are hiding.**

1. a b a n g w   <u>bang</u>

2. b a n k t y

3. h g k i n g

4. b s o n g m

5. f v s a n k

6. h a n g j b

7. s a r i n g

8. z l i n k n

9. b u n k x c

10. j h p i n k

10

9

8

7

6

5

4

3

2

1

These words all have **l** as a second letter.

Colour in your score on the testometer!

slide   fly   clock   black   glue

Write the new words you make.

1. Change the **fl** in **flip** to **sl**.   _slip_____

2. Change the **pl** in **plot** to **sl**. _____

3. Change the **sl** in **slat** to **fl**. _____

4. Change the **cl** in **click** to **fl**. _____

5. Change the **fl** in **flap** to **cl**. _____

6. Change the **bl** in **blink** to **cl**._____

7. Change the **cl** in **clot** to **bl**. _____

8. Change the **sl** in **slack** to **bl**._____

9. Change the **cl** in **class** to **gl**._____

10. Change the **cl** in **clad** to **gl**. _____

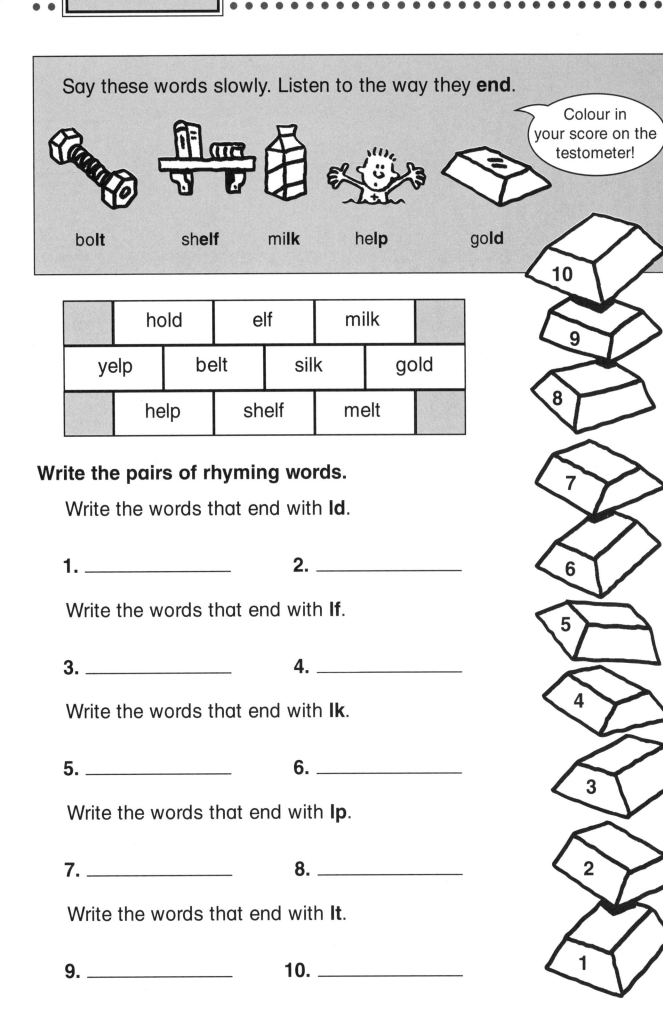

Say these words slowly. Listen to the way they **end**.

Colour in your score on the testometer!

bo**lt**   sh**elf**   mi**lk**   he**lp**   go**ld**

	hold	elf	milk	
yelp	belt	silk	gold	
	help	shelf	melt	

Write the pairs of rhyming words.

Write the words that end with **ld**.

1. _____   2. _____

Write the words that end with **lf**.

3. _____   4. _____

Write the words that end with **lk**.

5. _____   6. _____

Write the words that end with **lp**.

7. _____   8. _____

Write the words that end with **lt**.

9. _____   10. _____

10 9 8 7 6 5 4 3 2 1

Plural means when there is **more than one**.
We add **s** to many words to make them plural.

Colour in your score on the testometer!

one rabbit

lots of rabbits

Fill in the missing word.

1. one hat but two _____.

2. one leg but two _____.

3. one tin but two _____.

4. one pot but two _____.

5. one mug but two _____.

6. one _____ but two pans.

7. one _____ but two pets.

8. one _____ but two lips.

9. one _____ but two dogs.

10. one _____ but two sums.

Test 18 Sets of words

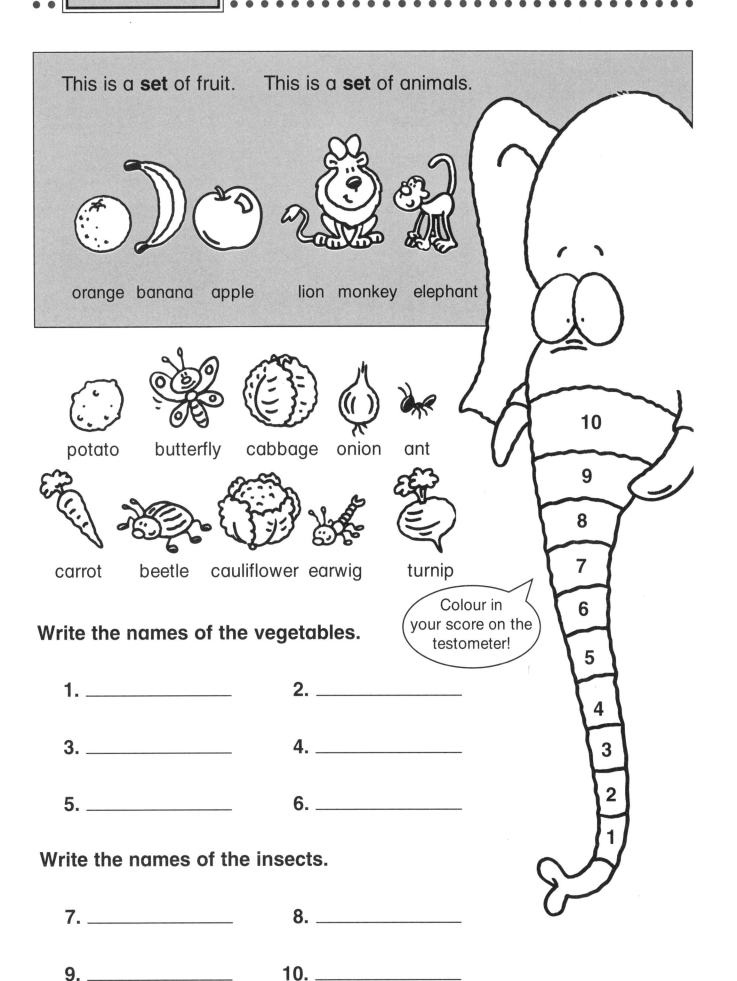

This is a **set** of fruit.   This is a **set** of animals.

orange banana apple   lion monkey elephant

potato   butterfly   cabbage   onion   ant

carrot   beetle   cauliflower earwig   turnip

Write the names of the vegetables.

Colour in
your score on the
testometer!

1. _____   2. _____

3. _____   4. _____

5. _____   6. _____

Write the names of the insects.

7. _____   8. _____

9. _____   10. _____

10
9
8
7
6
5
4
3
2
1

A **sentence** must make **sense**.

Colour in your score on the testometer!

The dog ate the bone. ☑   The bone ate the dog. ☒

Write each sentence correctly.

1. A cow barks. _____

2. A dog moos. _____

3. A duck hisses. _____

4. A horse cheeps. _____

5. A hen neighs. _____

6. A sheep chirps. _____

7. A snake quacks. _____

8. A bird bleats. _____

9. A bee brays. _____

10. A donkey buzzes. _____

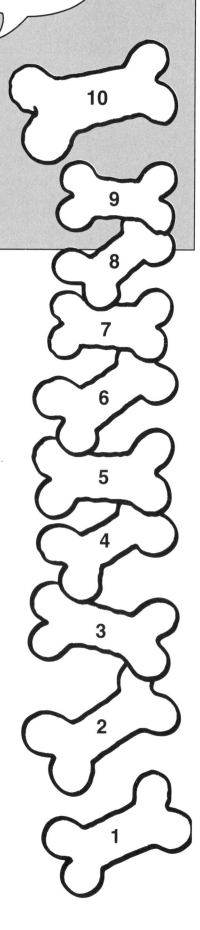

You will find **sh** and **ch** in many words.

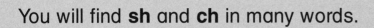

fi**sh** and **ch**ips

Colour in your score on the testometer!

Choose sh **or** ch **to complete each word.**

1. ____est

2. ____ell

3. ____ip

4. di____

5. ____eep

6. ben____

7. ____icken

8. tor____

9. ____eese

10. bru____

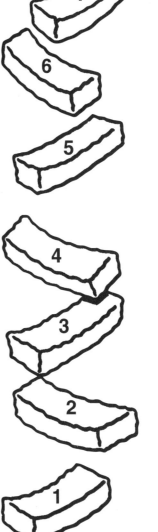

The letters **ee** and **oo** are two common letter patterns.

I have some b**oo**ts on my f**ee**t.

Colour in your score on the testometer!

Choose ee **or** oo **to complete each word.**

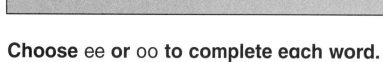

1. _____ l

2. st_____ l

3. p_____ l

4. br_____ m

5. m_____ n

6. tr_____

7. w_____ p

8. f___ d

9. sw_____ t

10. b_____

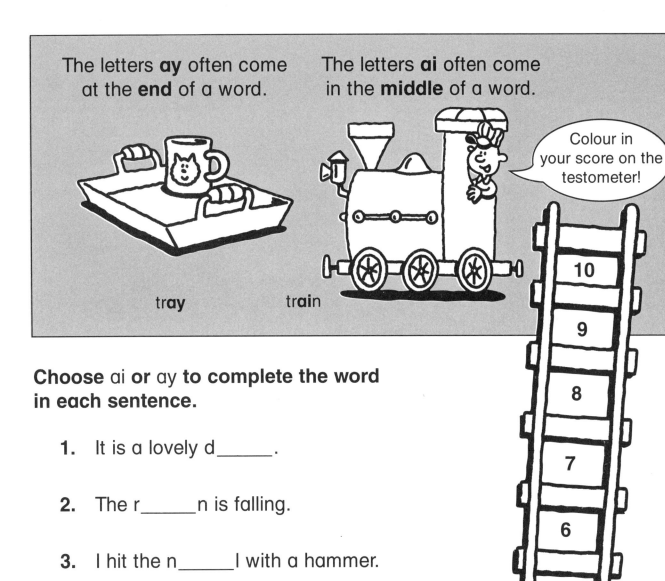

The letters **ay** often come at the **end** of a word.

The letters **ai** often come in the **middle** of a word.

tray

train

Colour in your score on the testometer!

Choose ai **or** ay **to complete the word in each sentence.**

1. It is a lovely d_____.

2. The r_____n is falling.

3. I hit the n_____l with a hammer.

4. You can swim in the b_____.

5. You can make things with cl_____.

6. The sn_____l went slowly.

7. I had to w_____t for my dinner.

8. You can pl_____ in the park.

9. The plates are on a tr_____.

10. You will have to w_____t and see.

10
9
8
7
6
5
4
3
2
1

There are **26** letters in the **alphabet**.

a	b	c	d	e	f	g	h	i	j	k	l	m
n	o	p	q	r	s	t	u	v	w	x	y	z

The five **vowels** are **a, e, i, o, u.**
All the other letters are called **consonants.**

Colour in your score on the testometer!

Fill in the missing vowel in each word.

1. m____t

2. s____n

3. b____d

4. n____t

5. b____b

6. b____g

7. f____x

6

8. s____x

9. m____d

10. b____n

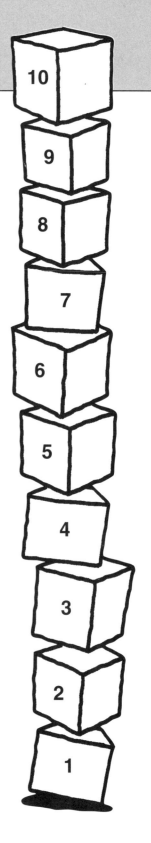

10
9
8
7
6
5
4
3
2
1

Test 24 — Names

Whenever we write **someone's name** we should always **start** with a **capital letter**.

Colour in your score on the testometer!

Humpty **D**umpty sat on a wall.

Write the names of these nursery rhyme characters correctly.

1. humpty dumpty _____

2. little bo peep _____

3. margery daw _____

4. tommy tucker _____

5. jack horner _____

6. polly _____

7. mary _____

8. lucy locket _____

9. georgie porgie _____

10. bobby shafto _____

10
9
8
7
6
5
4
3
2
1

We can add **ing** and **ed** to the ends of some words.

I am washing my face.
wash + ing = washing

Yesterday I washed my feet.
wash + ed = washed

Colour in your score on the testometer!

Add ing **to each word. Write the word you make.**

1. talk   _____

2. lick   _____

3. draw   _____

Add ed **to each word. Write the word you make.**

4. shout   _____

5. kick   _____

6. crawl   _____

Take the ing **off. Write the word you are left with.**

7. sniffing   _____

8. sleeping   _____

Take the ed **off. Write the word you are left with.**

9. turned   _____

10. passed   _____

A question must begin with a **capital letter** and end with a **question mark**.

Colour in your score on the testometer!

How many legs has a spider?

Write these questions correctly.

1. what is for tea

   _____

2. when are you coming

   _____

3. what shape is a ball

   _____

4. who is making that noise

   _____

5. where do you live

   _____

6. how many sweets have you got

   _____

7. what is your address

   _____

8. who is your teacher

   _____

9. when is it time for dinner

   _____

10. where is London

   _____

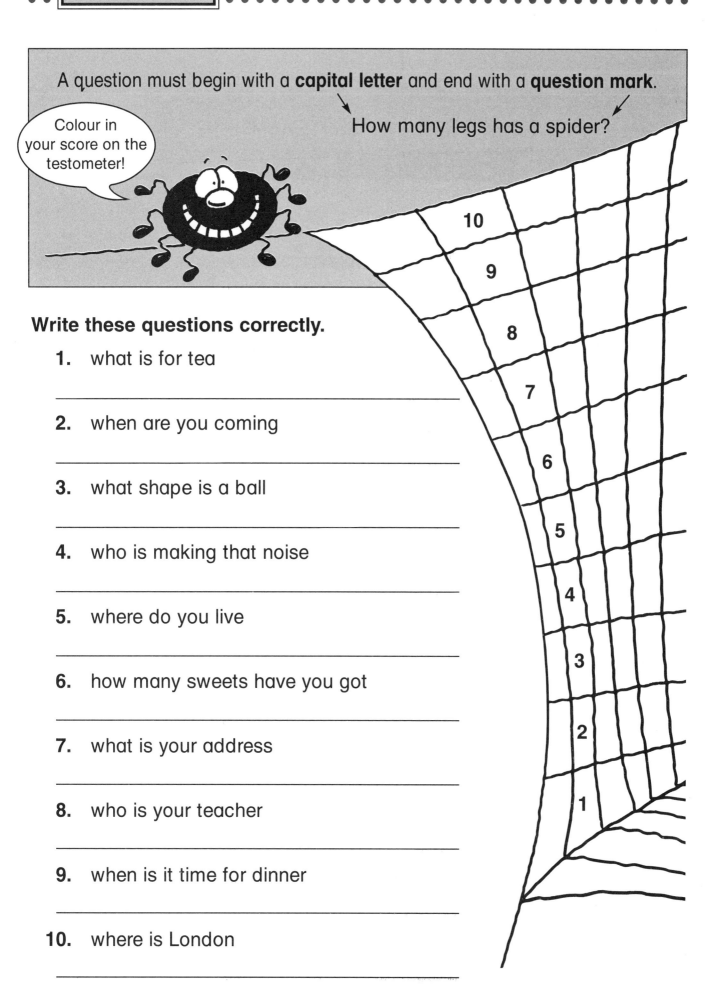

The two letter patterns **ea** and **oa** are **common**.

Colour in your score on the testometer!

a b**oa**t on the s**ea**

Write the new words you make.

1. Change the **s** in **sea** to **t**. _____

2. Change the **b** in **beat** to **s**. _____

3. Change the **l** in **leap** to **h**. _____

4. Change the **b** in **beak** to **l**. _____

5. Change the **t** in **teach** to **b**. _____

6. Change the **g** in **goat** to **b**. _____

7. Change the **f** in **foal** to **g**. _____

8. Change the **t** in **toad** to **r**. _____

9. Change the **c** in **coast** to **t**. _____

10. Change the **p** in **poach** to **c**. _____

Look what happens when we add **e** to the **end** of some words.

I hop**e** I can hop.

Colour in your score on the testometer!

hop + e = hope

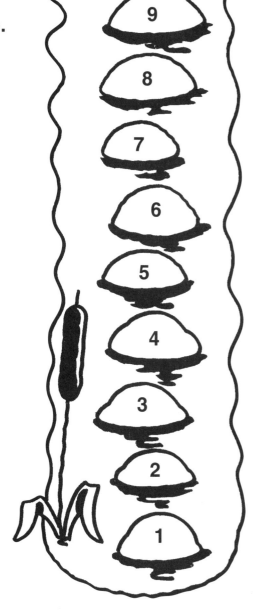

Do these sums. Write the words you make.

1. mad + e = _____

2. slid + e = _____

3. mak + e = _____

4. can + e = _____

5. cub + e = _____

6. rob + e = _____

7. shin + e = _____

8. cut + e = _____

9. tap + e = _____

10. bit + e = _____

It is important to know how to spell the **months of the year** correctly.

Colour in your score on the testometer!

Here are the months of the year in the wrong order.

August	May	December	January
February	June	October	March
September	April	November	July

Fill in the missing months in order.
Spell them correctly.

January

February

1. _____

2. _____

3. _____

4. _____

5. _____

6. _____

7. _____

8. _____

9. _____

10. _____

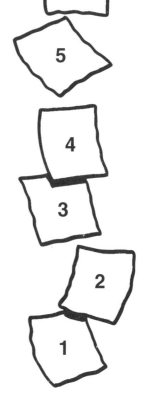

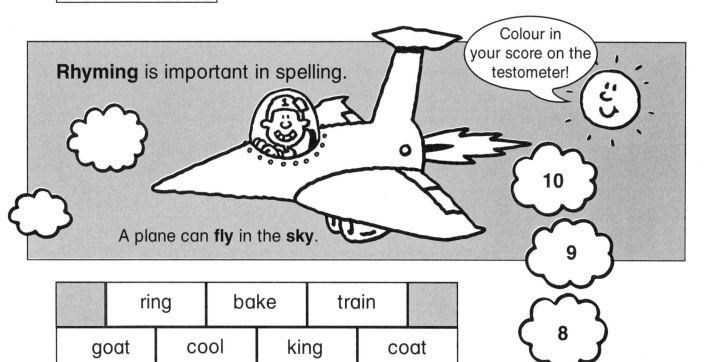

Rhyming is important in spelling.

A plane can **fly** in the **sky**.

	ring	bake	train	
goat	cool	king	coat	
	chain	pool	cake	

Write the pairs of rhyming words.

Write the **ing** words.

1. _____ 2. _____

Write the **ool** words.

3. _____ 4. _____

Write the **oat** words.

5. _____ 6. _____

Write the **ain** words.

7. _____ 8. _____

Write the **ake** words.

9. _____ 10. _____

Colour in your score on the testometer!

10

9

8

7

6

5

4

3

2

1

Answers

Test 1
1. c
2. g
3. i
4. m
5. p
6. s
7. t
8. v
9. x
10. z

Test 2
1. peg
2. pan
3. hop
4. pin
5. mat
6. hut
7. hen
8. mop
9. mug
10. pen

Test 3
1. sad
2. dig
3. bag
4. top
5. leg
6. fox
7. net
8. tub
9. dog
10. jug

Test 4
1. camel
2. horse
3. kangaroo
4. zebra
5. bear
6. tiger
7. monkey
8. goat
9. donkey
10. panda

Test 5
1. The sun is yellow.
2. The grass is green.
3. I like to read.
4. Hens lay eggs.
5. A lion can roar.
6. It is raining.
7. You swim in water.
8. You kick a ball.
9. The door is shut.
10. A tiger has stripes.

Test 6
1. bike
2. sun
3. star
4. money
5. banana
6. kangaroo
7. umbrella
8. cup
9. elephant
10. spade

Test 7
1. bag
2. map
3. zip
4. cup
5. hat
6. wig
7. net
8. dog
9. rug
10. pot

Test 8
1. bike
2. bus
3. car
4. lorry
5. rocket
6. helicopter
7. aeroplane
8. boat
9. yacht
10. ship

Test 9
1. fan
2. six
3. van
4. nod
5. leg
6. rod
7. peg
8. cut
9. mix
10. nut

Test 10
1. jam
2. tap
3. log
4. bun
5. tub
6. sob
7. ten
8. tin
9. bib
10. jet

Test 11
1. The rain falls.
2. A tree grows tall.
3. The sky is blue.
4. My cup is full.
5. A cow moos.
6. We like books.
7. You bang a drum.
8. It is sunny.
9. A ball is round.
10. I like to sing.

Test 12
1. off
2. puff
3. cuff
4. doll
5. bell
6. hill
7. fall
8. toss
9. hiss
10. fuss

Test 13
1. back
2. pack
3. neck
4. peck
5. kick
6. sick
7. lock
8. dock
9. luck
10. suck

Test 14
1. bang
2. bank
3. king
4. song
5. sank
6. hang
7. ring
8. link
9. bunk
10. pink

Test 15
1. slip
2. slot
3. flat
4. flick
5. clap
6. clink
7. blot
8. black
9. glass
10. glad

Test 16
1. hold
2. gold
3. elf
4. shelf
5. milk
6. silk
7. yelp
8. help
9. belt
10. melt